BRITAIN IN PICTURES
THE BRITISH PEOPLE IN PICTURES

THE BIRDS OF BRITAIN

GENERAL EDITOR
W. J. TURNER

The Editor is most grateful to all those who have
so kindly helped in the selection of illustrations
especially to officials of the various public
Museums Libraries and Galleries and
to all others who have generously
allowed pictures and MSS
to be reproduced

THE
BIRDS OF BRITAIN

JAMES FISHER

*WITH
12 PLATES IN COLOUR
AND
26 ILLUSTRATIONS IN
BLACK & WHITE*

COLLINS · 14 ST. JAMES'S PLACE · LONDON
MCMXLVII

PRODUCED BY
ADPRINT LIMITED LONDON

FIRST PUBLISHED 1942
FOURTH IMPRESSION 1947

PRINTED IN GREAT BRITAIN BY
CLARKE & SHERWELL LTD NORTHAMPTON
ON MELLOTEX BOOK PAPER MADE BY
TULLIS RUSSELL & CO LTD MARKINCH SCOTLAND

LIST OF ILLUSTRATIONS

PLATES IN COLOUR

ARCTIC TERN : (1835) by John James Laforest Audubon, 1770-1851
From Audubon's *Birds of America*, the most famous of all published collections of bird plates.

BRAMBLING : (1738) by Eleazar Albin, fl. 1713-1759
From Albin's *Natural History of Birds*, a good example of the early illustrated fauna, with plates hand-coloured by the artist and his daughter

BLACK-NECKED GREBE : (c. 1795) by Edward Donovan, 1768-1837
From Donovan's *Natural History of British Birds*. It is easy to detect that this drawing represents the black-necked and not, as Donovan thought, the eared grebe ; but it is a spirited example of his excellent and original plates

WOODLARK : (1821) by George Graves, fl. 1777-1834
From Grave's *British Ornithology*. This lively plate shows that the artist made some effort to break away from the atmosphere of taxidermy and death characteristic of the early faunas

GREEN WOODPECKER : (1852) by Benjamin Fawcett, 1808-1893. From Morris's *History of British Birds*, perhaps the most popular work on British birds ever issued. Fawcett, a fine printer and illustrator, drew and engraved his innumerable works with his own hand

GANNETS : (1836) by J. J. L. Audubon
From *Birds of America*. Audubon passed the Great Bird Rock, in the Gulf of St. Lawrence, on 14 July, 1833, and may well have made the sketches for this picture on the spot

KESTREL : (1862) by Joseph Wolf, 1820-1899
From Gould's *Birds of Great Britain*, which occupies much the same place in British ornithology as does the work of Audubon in America

LAPWING AND YOUNG : (1865) by John Gould
From his *Birds of Great Britain*. Gould spent great care and energy on his preliminary drawings, being particularly careful to make good pictures of the young of the wading birds —the first time such a thing had been attempted

GOLDFINCHES : (1863) by John Gould, 1804-1881
From *Birds of Great Britain*, the last great work conceived and largely executed by him ; the plates are in many ways the most naturalistic examples of his work

PARTRIDGE AND CHICKS : (1877) by Edward Neale, 1834-1904
From Dresser's *Birds of Europe*. No very great originality distinguishes Neale's style but he was a careful illustrator ; some of whose best work appeared in E. T. Booth's *Rough Notes on Birds*

DARTFORD WARBLERS : (1887) by John Gerrard Keulemans, 1842-1912
From Lilford's *Coloured Figures of the Birds of the British Islands*, the object of which was to collect in one book, pictures by the best contemporary bird artists, of all the birds known to visit Britain

RED GROUSE : (1908) by Archibald Thorburn, 1860-1935
From Millais' *Natural History of British Game Birds*. Thorburn early became the leading British ornithological artist. His pictures still form the basis of the standard field pocket-books and the present methods of identifying British birds in the field owe much to his drawings

BLACK & WHITE ILLUSTRATIONS

KINGFISHER
Wood engraving by A. Fussell and J. Thompson, 1840

A BIRD'S EYE VIEW OF BRITAIN

GILBERT WHITE, the curate of Selborne, introduced his Hampshire
parish to posterity with a catalogue of its natural features. There is
every reason that we should follow his example. Modern convention
might have it that the main character should, as it were, amble casually
in from the wings somewhere in Scene II. Britain cannot be so treated.
We cannot delay the description of what is the subject, and the scene, of this
essay—the countries of England, Wales and Scotland, and their place as the
home, and the support, of many different kinds of birds.

Great Britain, then, has about fifty-seven million acres. Roughly broken
down, they are as follows :—of moorland, deer forest and rough pasture, twenty
million ; of rich grassland, eighteen million ; of crops, twelve million ; of
parks and gardens and buildings, three and a half million ; of woodland and
scrub, three million ; of inland water, half a million. Nobody knows the
exact length of Britain's coast-line. Three thousand five hundred miles is a
conservative estimate. There are a thousand isles big enough to graze a sheep,
or raise a crop on.

Every spring about a hundred and twenty million land-birds take up terri-
tories, build nests, and raise their young upon these fifty-seven million acres.
A pair of birds to an acre, on an average. Every spring many millions of sea-

7

birds come to the cliffs and rocks and islands and beaches. Statistically-minded ornithologists are trying hard to count these seabirds, but have not got very far ; there are many tens of millions, perhaps even hundreds of millions ; that is all that they can say. Four hundred and twenty-four different species have been admitted to the British List. They have been seen on the British Isles at one time or another, by somebody held to be reliable.

Of these, one hundred and thirty-five are resident. All these breed with us, and are found here also in the winter ; five of them were introduced by man. Every spring, with unfailing regularity, the migrants come from the warmer south. Fifty-one species of these summer visitors breed regularly in Britain. Two summer visitors (the great and sooty shearwaters) come regularly, but do not breed—they have already nested in the Southern Atlantic ocean.

Forty-eight other kinds come in the winter from the wilder north or pass along our shores on regular passage roads. Some are rare, but those who know the habits of migrants can go to the right place, and will not fail to see them. One hundred and sixty-one sorts are so occasional, so irregular, in their visits to Britain (whether on chance passage, weather-borne, lost, strayed or eccentric) that a sight of them means a thrill, an excitement, a letter to the Editor. Twenty-six further species have only been reliably reported once in the country. One, the great auk, is extinct.

Of all these species, then, only about half play anything like an important part in the web of British wild life. About a hundred land-birds ; about a hundred sea or water birds. These two hundred sorts of birds are perhaps the most written of, the most poeticised, the most sung of, dreamed of, listened to, observed, protected, loved, birds in the world. These few tens of millions of birds have a public not many times smaller, in numbers, than themselves.

Well over half Britain's fifty-seven million acres are cultivated, or built on, by man. Thirty million acres are under crops, lie fallow, or give permanent grazing to cattle and sheep. Over two and a half million acres are built-up areas. Over half a million acres are parks, or orchards, or gardens ; another half million are inland waters ; a further million waste, scrubland and swamp. The mountains and highlands are twenty million acres of rough grazing, deer forest and moor. Woodlands once clothed nearly all the face of England— now there are little more than a couple of million acres in the whole of Britain.

The birds of Britain are distributed by no means evenly over these habitats. In each type of country we find a special group of birds, and each of these groups contains about the same number of species. Usually the number is about thirty. But though the number of different sorts may be the same in each habitat, the number of individuals may be quite different. For instance, on heath and moorland there is seldom more than a single bird living on every two acres ; but in some gardens there may be as many as ten on one acre— and in some special garden sanctuaries there may be thirty. When the bird population of gardens is swollen by the presence of a colony of social birds, like rooks, there may be over a hundred birds to the acre.

ARCTIC TERN
Illustration by J. J. L. Audubon, 1835, from his *Birds of America*

BRAMBLING

Illustration by Eleazar Albin, 1738, from his *Natural History of Birds*

Visitors to Britain from the United States, or from the continent of Europe, often comment on our tiny fields, and on our miles of roads and lanes and hedgerows. These hedgerows mean a lot to birds. The birds of agricultural land (it is safe to say) are not faced with very serious difficulties in finding food. Most small birds feed their young on insects in the breeding season, and it is pretty clear that in most parts the supply well exceeds the demand. Their main trouble is to find a place to establish a territory, defend it from others, and within (or near) it build a nest. The hedges and gardens supply the nest-places, and the headquarters from which to proclaim ownership by song. The fields of the continental countries are vast, open, often fenced—and quiet. The fields of England are small, hedgebound, and full of the song of many birds.

Britain, then, has much cultivation ; much moorland ; a little woodland that is left to it after years of cutting and grazing, with little planting ; a little fen and marsh land in such places as the low lands of Lincolnshire, Cambridge-shire, Norfolk and Kent—little, indeed, is left after over a hundred years of intensive draining and reclamation ; a fair amount of inland water ; and a prodigious coastline. Hence the breeding stock of wild birds is rich in those species which inhabit moors ; in those which have adapted themselves to life in agricultural land—and most of these like robins, blackbirds, warblers, probably came to the fields, when the fields were made and tilled, from woods and scrub ; in sea- and shore-birds : is fairly rich in freshwater birds—those that breed by the side of lakes and rivers and streams : is poor (now) in marsh-birds.

MERLIN
Wood engraving by G. E. Lodge, 1895

THE PECULIARITY OF BRITISH BIRDS

EXACTLY a hundred of the 133 resident breeding birds of the British Isles are precisely the same as those which live in neighbouring countries. The other 33 are peculiar to Britain—that is they are different enough from their nearest relatives on the continent to be classed as separate subspecies. There is a consistent, and easily recognisable difference, for instance, between the British and the Continental goldfinch ; between the English and Continental nuthatch ; between the Scottish and Continental crossbill. Furthermore, one species (as opposed to mere subspecies) of bird is confined to our islands. The red grouse is found on the moors of England, Wales, Scotland and Ireland and nowhere else in the world—except in one place in Germany where it was introduced from Britain. The British are proud of the grouse, and make great sport with it ; round this famous bird has been built a little industry, a little cult, of which more later.

Even within the boundaries of Britain we find populations of birds with local peculiarities. The colours of the Irish jay are darker and more vivid than those of the jays of the rest of our islands. Irish coal tits have yellow cheeks, not white. Irish dippers are darker. The islands of Shetland, of the Outer Hebrides, and of St. Kilda each have their own peculiar wrens. Those of St. Kilda have been made much of ; compared with the mainland form, they are a good deal larger, less russet, more heavily barred on the back, less dark below. When our party visited St. Kilda in 1939 we were able to confirm another difference, which cannot be examined on skins. The St. Kilda wrens have a very much louder and more penetrating song than the mainland wrens. Wrens have to sing, for the same reasons as other birds—to proclaim ownership of territory, to cement the sexual bond. On St. Kilda they have to register their title deeds against the rumbling, roaring Atlantic.

When the St. Kilda wren was first described, in 1884, the ornithologist Seebohm gave it the rank of a full species. It is the opinion of most workers, to-day, that it does not quite deserve this—and in one sense its reduction to a subspecies may have done it some good. For in the years after its first description it was much sought after by collectors. As a mere subspecies it has not, perhaps, been so popular. St. Kilda is now a sanctuary, and the wrens are doing well. In 1931, the year after the human inhabitants left the islands, there were certainly sixty-eight pairs. In 1939 our count gave almost exactly the same answer for the world population of this little, hardy bird.

Britain, then, has its own special birds. Mostly, these special birds are not *very* different from those of the Continent ; but they are peculiar, in the old sense of the word. One, the grouse, is quite peculiar. And the study of the peculiarities of British tits and creepers, of Hebridean rock pipits and stonechats, of Shetland starlings and snipe, is telling zoologists interesting and useful facts about evolution.

GREAT AUK
Wash drawing by Daniel King, c. 1652
The earliest known figure of the great auk

There is nothing tropical about England. The British climate is temperate and constant. No tropical birds come to us ; but the great majority of European temperate-zone birds exploit our land fully. And, on some mountain-tops and sea-cliffs, breed birds which are truly arctic. The chough, a southern bird which ranges from the Canary Islands to the coasts of north-west France, pushes its northern outposts up the west coast of Britain as far as the Inner Hebrides. A bird of the Mediterranean, the cirl bunting, reaches its northern limit, on the continent, in Belgium and south-west Germany. In Britain it breeds in good numbers, though locally, through the south, and the west country, and finds its limit in North Wales, well north of its continental range. The Dartford warbler breeds mainly in Hampshire and Surrey, but extends into Berkshire and has even bred, fairly often, as far north as Shropshire. On the continent the races of this warmth-loving species of bird extend from north Africa no further than Brittany—yet in England the species is resident—our only resident warbler, in fact. It is clear, then, that some species of birds that are accustomed to Mediterranean warmth find the British isles tolerable—more tolerable than lesser latitudes on the continent. It must be admitted, however, that this is not always so. For instance the nightingale, in England, struggles to keep a foothold in northern Lincolnshire, and goes no further north. On the continent it keeps more than level. The woodlark breeds well north in Norway, Sweden and Finland yet in Britain fares badly beyond central Wales. North of the Humber British nuthatches are few ; there are none in Scotland—yet one of the continental races breeds, in Norway, at a latitude north of Shetland.

11

It is clear, then, that Britain has birds which are Mediterranean, and birds which are mid-European. It also has arctic and alpine birds. A sub-arctic species, the twite or mountain linnet, has a continental race which is practically confined to Norway, where it goes far north. In the British isles it is found fairly widely on mountain ranges, and it comes, in Scotland, down to sea-level in some rocky places. The snow-bunting, the most truly arctic of all buntings, breeds all round the arctic regions. It seldom comes further south than the arctic circle; in Norway it only goes as far down as the latitude of Shetland, as a breeder. In Scotland it breeds as far south as Perthshire and Argyll, though, admittedly mostly on the higher mountain-tops. A sub-arctic hawk, the merlin, breeds far north in Scandinavia, and even in Novaya Zemlya—in Britain it breeds on most wide stretches of moor, even, sometimes, on Dartmoor and Exmoor. In central Europe the ptarmigan haunts only the alpine mountain-tops, and in the arctic it is the only game bird. In Scotland it breeds on the mountains, in the comparable, tundra-like, alpine zone of vegetation.

Among the British sea-birds two stand out as being essentially arctic. The bonxie, or great skua, has its main home in Iceland and the Faeroes. In Britain it breeds in Shetland, has recently extended to Orkney, and may soon be breeding again on the mainland of Scotland, where it did many years ago. But the fulmar is a more spectacular example. It is truly a bird of the high arctic: of the arctic islands of Greenland, Spitsbergen, Bear Island, Jan Mayen, Franz Josef Land, Novaya Zemlya (the catalogue could be continued). In historical times it had, until a hundred to a hundred and twenty-five years ago, only one more southerly outpost. There was a big colony on St. Kilda. Some time between 1816 and 1839 fulmars began to colonise the Faeroes, and in 1878 they arrived in Shetland and began to breed on new British cliffs. The spread has continued in a most remarkable fashion, round the British coasts. Nearly all the coasts of Scotland and Ireland, where the scene is rough and oceanic, have now fallen. Most suitable parts of the east coast of England now have fulmars breeding. In Wales, on the coasts of the West Country, and even over the Channel, at Ushant in France, the fulmars are coming to cliffs in the breeding season, and investigating them. It will only be a matter of time before they breed in these places—and not a very long time.

Britain is a great breakwater that slants out from the main mass of the continent into the Atlantic. Its free end (as it were), the north of Scotland, is in a direct line with the northern coast of Norway. Owing to this particular geographical position Britain attracts two special groups of birds. It draws, and makes a breeding ground for the Atlantic birds, the ocean wanderers; and it draws and guides the Scandinavian land-birds, the passage migrants.

From the wide seas, where they soar and glide and ride the gales, the kittiwakes and Manx shearwaters, those little albatrosses the fulmars, the storm petrels, the Leach's fork-tailed petrels—all the wind-sailors of the northern ocean make for the British coast when the breeding season comes. The auks— the puffins, guillemots and razorbills, which swim like penguins, and whose

BLACK-NECKED GREBE
Illustration by Edward Donovan, c. 1795, from his *Natural History of British Birds*

WOODLARK
Illustration by George Graves, from his *British Ornithology*, 1821

clumsy-looking flight is purposeful, and more efficient than it appears—come to the great seabird stations in millions ; to the lonely Atlantic islands of the outer chain—Unst, Foula, Rona and Sula Sgeir, the Flannans, St. Kilda, Barra Head, Inishtrahull, Tory Island, the Blaskets, the Skelligs, the Bull and the Cow, Lundy ; to the inner isles—Handa, Ailsa Craig, the Skerries, Great Saltee, the Farnes, the Bass Rock; Hoy, Copinsay, Noss ; to the great mainland cliffs —Cape Wrath, Horn Head, Moher, Land's End, Bempton, Fowlsheugh, Great Orme. Almost a special species of ornithologist has evolved round the study of cliffs and islands, and their populations of birds—a species adapted to travel in many ways, accustomed to sail and manage boats, to climb and swim, and to talk for hours with those natural bird-watchers, the lighthouse-keepers. Two of the best of our nature writers to-day, Lockley and Fraser Darling, belong very definitely to this species. Many bird-watchers have almost a mania for 'collecting' islands and rocks—perhaps Malcolm Stewart or Lockley has the best collection. I have not collected such a bad lot myself, at one time or another.

Every spring the migrants come north from their winter countries, from Africa and the Mediterranean shores. The passage is on a broad front, but not an even front. To a great extent the migrants have fixed routes—they come, more or less, in rivers. And in autumn, swollen in numbers by their offspring, they return, not as floods, but as deeper rivers along the same routes. The passage-rivers flow, in Britain, mainly along the coasts, the east coast more than the west. Certain strips of coast, and certain islands, form bottlenecks, where the river is very deep. At these places the watchers gather.

It is only natural that the bird watchers should go to observe migration at the places where it is most obvious and exciting. It is not surprising that a distinct cult of the bottleneck-place, the 'migration-station' should have developed. Historically, the trend dates from about the turn of the present century, when various enthusiasts began to realise the value of coastal stations, and exploit them ; from this time, too, dates the use of lighthouse-keepers as spies and intelligence officers. Some of the British migration stations are so good that they have been developed as permanent places of observation, with built-in, harmless traps for catching and identifying rare warblers and other small birds, (afterwards they are marked with light aluminium rings and released). Until the war broke out, organised parties of ornithologists regularly visited the following places, in autumn and sometimes also in spring, for the purpose of taking routine observations on the passage of birds :—Dungeness in Kent, Blakeney Point and Scolt Head in Norfolk, Holy Island off Northumberland, the Isle of May off Fife, the Fair Isle in Shetland ; and, on the west coast, R. M. Lockley kept a migration station going on Skokholm, off Pembrokeshire.

One of the incidental effects of this concentration on bottlenecks in the main migratory routes is that the list of British birds has been considerably enlarged. Rarities which play no real part in the British fauna have been noted or collected at these stations. Sometimes these rarities have been proved to have regular,

13

PUFFIN
Wood engraving by Thomas Bewick, 1804

tiny passages along the British coast ; sometimes they have been, without any sort of doubt, weather-borne wanderers driven from their normal routes. To give an example, of the eighteen land-birds which have only been recorded *once* in Britain, fourteen were collected on the main east coast passage-route. Of these the famous bottleneck of Fair Isle provides three (pine-bunting, paddy-field warbler, booted warbler). North Ronaldshay in Orkney gives another ; Northumberland one ; the Yorkshire coast two ; one seaside place in Lincoln-shire two more ; Norfolk coast two ; Kent coast one (also two water-birds, all in the Dungeness-Romney Marsh area) ; Sussex coast two. Of the four remaining, only two were taken inland—the Egyptian nightjar in Nottingham-shire, and the masked shrike at Woodchurch in Kent. To end the list, the only two such birds taken on the west have been Pallas's grasshopper-warbler, at the Rockabill Lighthouse, Dublin, and the American nightjar (or nighthawk) at Trescoe in the Scillies.

So intense is the study of migration to-day that it seems almost fantastic that, not much more than a hundred and fifty years ago, naturalists were con-founded and confused by serious doubts and difficulties about migration. They had little knowledge of the facts—and counterbalanced this by the wildness of their theories. The open-mindedness and intelligent puzzlement of Gilbert White, on the subject (1789) and the ingenuity of John Legg (1780) contrast very strikingly with the attitudes of many of their contemporaries. Legg and White, and Thomas Pennant, compiler of the standard textbook of that time, really did more than any others to rescue the study of migration from the hibernation theories of Hunter, or the birds-to-the-moon ideas of Morton. Between them, they suggested the modern technique of station-observation. All that has needed to be added is the technique of marking.

14

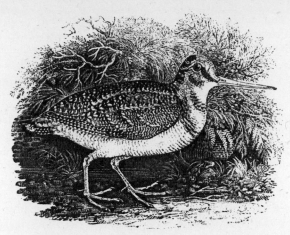

WOODCOCK
Wood engraving by Thomas Bewick, 1804

In 1890 a private landowner began a study of the movements of woodcock by marking young birds, in nests in Northumberland, with aluminium rings round their legs. In the next twenty years more ambitious, organized schemes began on the continent. The British bird-marking scheme started in 1909— and since then well over half a million birds have been ringed in this country, almost entirely by private, voluntary workers who pay for the privilege (which they consider it to be) of taking part in the scheme by buying the rings. In 1939, just before the war broke out, the number of birds ringed yearly had reached the record figure of 55,817. About half of these birds have been ringed as young in the nest, about half as adults, caught in specially designed traps. The trapping of adult birds gives better returns than the ringing of young, since the most dangerous time for a bird is in the first few months of its life, while it is a nestling or a fledgling ; owing to the high mortality at this time many rings, placed on young birds, are wasted. Hence many keen country-living ornithologists have started their own little trapping-stations—some of them ring over a thousand birds in a year—and many societies run traps, with a rota of watchers. For instance, the Oxford Ornithological Society has for many years kept trapping stations going in the University parks, has ringed at these a very large number of adult birds, and has had a very satisfactory number of recoveries from other parts of the British Isles and from foreign countries. At some of the coastal migration-stations large funnel-like Heligoland traps have been used with success ; these are great, long, wire-netting funnels whose wide ends embrace some bushy cover. The passage-migrants— or at all events the smaller perching birds from among them—work through the cover during their stay at the station, and many of them reach that part which leads to the trap. It is a fairly simple matter to drive them, then, down

15

to the narrow end, where a slide drops behind them and they can be caught up, handled, examined and marked. These big funnel traps, as their name implies, were first developed at Heligoland—an island which is perhaps the most famous passage-bottleneck of all Europe ; in Britain they have been used on Holy Island, the Isle of May, Skokholm ; and a site has been selected for one at the Fair Isle.

The study of migration in Britain is only directed in part towards the birds of passage, and the exciting and interesting routes along which they pass. More fundamental, perhaps, is the concern with which British naturalists, ever since the dawn of natural history recording, have noted the dates of arrival and departure of our fifty-odd summer visitors, and our winter visitors. Such diaries and calendars and lists, as are of use, go back to the seventeenth century. So busy, indeed, have naturalists been that to-day we can plot the broad-front spring spread of birds like swallows and willow-warblers over the whole of Europe ; taking the points where observers have been stationed, and plotting the dates on which the first large influx of the migrants has been noted. By April first, for instance, the swallows have arrived in most of France ; by the fifteenth they have reached nearly all Germany, though, in Britain, only the channel counties, the west country, and south-west Ireland. By the first of May they have progressed little further in western Europe, but have filled Ireland and have reached the highlands of Scotland. By 15 May the swallows are everywhere in Britain, and present throughout southern Scandinavia. By June the first they are beyond the arctic circle, in northern Norway, Finland and the U.S.S.R. This full distance they travel in about 77 days—two thousand miles—keeping almost perfect step with the temperature 48 degrees Fahrenheit ; being ahead of it only in the western coastal districts, and behind only in the hilly parts.

That such a detailed analysis could be made (by H. N. Southern, an enterprising British zoologist) shows what a lot of information can be got from the analysis of simple field records. The industrious naturalists of the past, recording dates of arrival and departure, recording the weather and the flowering of plants, did so for their own pleasure and edification, and with little other motive. They would be intrigued to know what use can now be made of their observations. To-day, the compilation of these sorts of records is becoming highly organised ; for instance, the Royal Meteorological Society asks for them every year, so that it can compile a phenological report for the country ; and many natural history societies make a routine of collecting this kind of information. And every year there are more and more Letters to the Editor, and Fourth Leaders in *The Times*, about the first hearing of the chiffchaff, the willow-warbler, the blackcap, the cuckoo ; the first sight of the swallow, the swift, the turtle-dove. For these are the birds that people like—the birds that come with summer—and people write down, or tell others about what they like. "Chiffchaff's come," says the gardener, "in Rectory garden" ; and he smiles and nods his head in a solemn, knowing way.

LONG-EARED OWLS
Drawing by Joseph Wolf, engraved by Richter, 1873

17

DOTTERELS
Drawing by John Gould, engraved by Richter, 1862

HISTORICAL CHANGES

IF we are to make the most of the communities of birds in Britain we must give them some sort of historical background. We must go back to the last Ice Age, which ended perhaps fifteen thousand years ago. During the Ice Age itself Britain was connected with the continent ; and it was icy, with alpine-arctic plants and animals. As the ice retreated, the tree-line rose, but the trees and the communities they supported were of the north—the trees were pine and birch, and they spread to the south of our islands. By historical times the northern trees had retreated, more or less to Scotland, to be replaced in England by oak forests. Man soon got busy on the northern trees, and on the oak, cutting and clearing ; cultivated land gradually became dominant. To-day as our earlier statistics show, we have a land clothed mainly by tillage and moor, with relics, only, of the earlier successions. The Britain of the Ice Age is now found only on mountain-tops ; the northern pine and birch in Scotland, much reduced by cutting and grazing and burning, is now found in its primeval state only in a few places like the Spey Valley ; the oak of Old England survives, as it used to be, in a few sanctuaries like the New Forest ; elsewhere fire and the plough, cattle and sheep, have taken charge. Where there are once again woods, these are planted, mostly with foreign trees—larch, spruce, fir, beech. And in the low lands of East Anglia, the Wash and Norfolk, man's enterprise has turned miles of wild marsh and fen into rich, drained, fertile soil ; only in a few places, like the Broads and Wicken and Woodwalton, is the ancient fenland left.

18

CROSSBILLS
Drawing by John Gould, engraved by Richter, 1864

Each of these different successions, these once-dominant associations of plants, had its own fauna of birds. The birds have suffered the changes in different ways. They have sometimes given in, as it were, and disappeared. Or they have hung on, as relics. Or they have changed their habits, and struck

19

COAL TIT
Wood engraving by Thomas Bewick, 1797

out into the new habitat that replaced the old. In the ice-age, alpine zone of the high Scottish mountain-tops we still find three relict birds, ptarmigan, snow-bunting and dotterel. The ptarmigan is still pretty abundant on suitable mountains ; the small amount of attention it receives from sportsmen does not appear to harm it. The snow-bunting does less well, nests on fewer mountains, but certainly does not seem to be in much danger of extinction. The dotterel is hanging on in the Grampians and a few other parts of Scotland, and there are one or two pairs, high up, in the Lake District.

The birds of the ancient birch of the post-ice-age Britain do not all appear to have survived, though it is difficult to tell exactly what they were in the absence of human recorders at that period. However we can surmise a little, by comparison with the birds of the Scandinavian birchwoods. It seems fairly clear that Britain has lost the redwing, that beautiful thrush of the north, and the handsome brambling as breeding species owing to the disappearance of the birch. To-day, the redwing and brambling are common winter visitors—but have only bred once or twice in this country, in the last hundred years. The black grouse, another birchland bird, managed to carry on very well on scrub-bound moors until lately. Now it is getting very rare, and is fast disappearing from its former breeding-places. The lesser redpoll, on the other hand, seems to have been able to adapt itself to the new order, by colonising new habitats—to-day it is a fairly common bird of deciduous woodlands and plantations, and breeds in them.

The fauna of the old pine forests almost certainly included crossbills, siskins and crested tits ; capercaillies ; long-eared owls ; coal and willow tits, tree-creepers and goldcrests. The first three of these have behaved as relics—they

20

GREEN WOODPECKER

Illustration by Benjamin Fawcett, 1852, from Morris's *History of British Birds*

GANNETS

Illustration by J. J. L. Audubon, 1836, from his *Birds of America*

REDWING
Wood engraving by A. Fussell and J. Thompson, 1838

have not struck out, to any great extent, into the later habitats. The cross-bill appears to be the most conservative—it is confined almost entirely to the forests of the Spey valley, where it is quite abundant. Provided it is properly looked after, it should maintain its status without difficulty. The Scottish crossbill is distinct from the Continental crossbill; the latter invades England from the mainland of Europe about every ten years or so (its numbers undergo cyclical fluctuations), and within the last fifty years or more has started small breeding-colonies in some English pine plantations, which are doing quite well. The Scottish crested tit, another relic whose real home is in the Spey valley forests, has lately been found to be breeding in new places in the Highlands, and its status is not in danger. The siskin has an even wider distribution in Scottish conifer woods—it now breeds in quite a number of plantations—and though technically it is a relic, it seems to be fairly adaptable.

The capercaillie, another bird of old pinewoods, has had a chequered career. By about 1760 it was completely extinct in Scotland and Ireland. Probably hunting may have had something to do with its extinction, though I believe that the disappearance of most of its habitat must have been primarily to blame. In 1837 it was re-introduced in Perthshire, from Sweden, and has since spread back into the pinewoods, both ancient and planted, over quite a large area of Scotland; it is once more a sporting bird, and can suffer winter shooting.

It is very likely that when the pinewood was dominant over the whole of the British Isles, the long-eared owl was the most abundant species of owl.

SCOTTISH CRESTED TIT
Water colour drawing by Henrik Grönvold, 1880

When the pine began to disappear it probably did not recede with it, as did some of the birds I have just mentioned. Instead, it made quite a job of colonising the deciduous woods. To-day it is fairly abundant over the whole of Britain. It nests of course, in pine woods, both natural and planted, but it also nests equally well in oak woods and beech woods. In Ireland it is still the commonest owl and nests everywhere where there are groups of considerable trees of any sort.

The other four pinewood birds—the two tits, the creeper and the goldcrest, have successfully conquered several new habitats ; coal tits and willow tits are now found in all sorts of woodland, natural or planted, as well as in agricultural land and gardens. Unfortunately we do not know as much as we would like about the distribution of the willow tit outside Scotland, since it is so difficult to distinguish from the marsh tit.

The New Forest gives a picture of what England must have been like in early English and mediaeval days when the oak was its dominant plant. Great trees of all ages, some low and spreading with gnarls and holes, some tall and straight, with many smaller bushes and herbs growing between. This English

22

SISKINS
Drawing by J. Gould, engraved by W. Hart, 1867

oakland provides almost perfect cover for birds and it is not surprising that it is richer in bird life than any other type of British woodland. Besides the species of birds that certainly colonised it from the departing pinewoods, we find eight or nine sorts which are quite characteristic of this habitat. Some of

23

these species do not breed in pinewoods at all, and must have arrived in the British Isles only at the succession; nuthatches, marsh tits, lesser spotted woodpeckers all fall into this category. The other species present include some of our most beautiful singing birds, birds which make half the romance and atmosphere of the spring woods, birds like the garden warbler, blackcap, wood warbler, chiffchaff, and the nightingale. There are other birds which properly belong to broad-leaved woodland, bullfinches, great and blue tits, green woodpeckers, but these are found in other habitats, and are therefore not quite so typical.

So far we have not mentioned the species of birds which are to-day dominant in Great Britain. It is probably fair to say that chaffinches, blackbirds, robins, hedge sparrows, and song thrushes, all of which have larger numbers than any of the species which we have so far mentioned, owe their commanding position to the existence of agricultural land. Historically these species certainly came from the woods and scrub; mostly from the broad-leaved woods and the days of the oak. According to the most reliable counts of breeding birds in a large number of samples of selected types of land in Britain, it appears that the commonest and most abundant land birds of all are chaffinches and blackbirds. Their numbers appear to be almost exactly the same. There are probably about ten million of each in England and Wales; robins are not much less abundant.

Starlings number about the same as robins and are very much parasites on domestic and agricultural man. So are house sparrows, though they have less than one-third the numbers of chaffinches, and less than one-half the numbers of robins. House sparrows, hedge sparrows, song thrushes and meadow pipits number about three million each. The last named, the meadow pipit, is alone amongst those we have so far discussed in belonging to moorland, where it is absolutely the dominant species—as we have seen the general bird population of moorland is low compared with that of the other habitats.

To sum up so far. In the last fifteen thousand years, Britain has passed out of an ice age, through a pinewood age, then through an oakwood age, and then into an agricultural age. Relics of these ages still persist in various parts of Britain, and with them certain of the original birds. With the succession of each age by the next, some birds have disappeared, others have hung on to the little that was left, while others have adapted themselves to the new order. The final present-day bird community is the least natural, the most man-made; it is based on the wide and drastic effects of man's use of tools. This agricultural land has taken over birds almost entirely from woodland, and mainly from oakland at that. It has shuffled species round a bit, some, well adapted to woodland, appear not to have been so well pre-adapted to agricultural land. Of the two completely dominant birds, the blackbird probably comes from oak woods, and the chaffinch from the pinewoods; they are now masters of every wood, copse, spinney, field, hedge, garden and park in the land.

By courtesy of the London Library

KESTREL

Illustration by Joseph Wolf, 1862, from Gould's *Birds of Great Britain*

LAPWING AND YOUNG

Illustration by John Gould, 1865, from his *Birds of Great Britain*

ROBIN
Wood engraving by Thomas Bewick, 1797

I have made a point of these historical changes, since in my view the present birds of Britain can be best pictured in the perspective of change. So far I have dealt with a series of great natural changes, only the last of which has been due to man. The last one, indeed, appears to have been quite as radical as the others. There is scarcely an acre in Britain where man has not altered the habitat, and with it the bird life. One complete bird community which we have so far not mentioned in detail, has been completely upset by man. This is the community of the marshes and fens.

Unlike most of the woodland birds, the marsh birds have been unable to exploit new habitats when their own has been removed by man. In the period up to the end of the Renaissance, cranes, spoonbills, ruffs, avocets, Savi's warblers, —probably, also, aquatic and melodious warblers—were part of the British bird fauna. In earlier times there may even have been pelicans in East Anglia. Since the great drainage schemes of the seventeenth century these birds have disappeared, one after another, and now no longer breed. Some others are still relics—so few that their numbers can be guessed fairly closely (mostly under one hundred)—like marsh and Montagu's harriers, black-tailed godwits, bitterns, bearded tits. Conservation has rescued these in the nick of time ; a few sanctuaries, snatched from the tentacles of utilitarian agriculture and saved from draining, now support them.

Spoonbills, then, used to breed in several marshy places in England in the sixteenth century. They were even nesting in Fulham in 1523. By the middle of the seventeenth century they were making their last stand in Norfolk and Suffolk. Cranes had become extinct even earlier—about 1600. On saltings at eastern British river-mouths from the Humber southwards the avocet

BITTERN
Wood engraving by A. Fussell and J. Thompson, 1840

bred until about 1843, when the last breeding pair was recorded in Kent—until two pairs appeared "somewhere in Ireland" in 1938 and bred within a few yards of each other ! The ruff hung on, as a regular breeding bird in Norfolk marshes, until 1871 ; perhaps a dozen pairs have nested since then in odd years.

Of the relics, perhaps the marsh harrier is the next on the list for extinction. Though there are possibly a few pairs in Norfolk and Suffolk to-day whose presence is (rightly) being kept a secret, and whose breeding is not being publicly recorded, it seems clear that, at the most, four or five pairs—and in some years one or none—have annually bred in Britain during the present century. Montagu's harrier, another relic, is in better case. It appears that this species does not require so great an area of unbroken marshland, as the other harrier, for success. Anyway it still breeds in at least half a dozen counties every year.

26

RUFFS AND REEVE
Drawing by J. Gould, engraved by W. Hart, 1871

The black-tailed godwit, at one time, appeared to have met the fate of the spoonbill and ruff. Over a hundred years ago it had ceased to breed, regularly, in the fenland. Since 1829 there are only scattered records, in certain years, of its breeding in any place in the British Isles. All the same, though it did not breed, it continued to visit Britain in fair numbers, mainly on passage, though quite often in winter, and sometimes, as a non-breeder, in summer. Lately its visits have been getting more frequent; a pair may have bred in Norfolk in 1934, another pair laid eggs in 1937, and a pair, or pairs are now breeding in Lincolnshire. So the black-tailed godwit may have come back; let us hope it has.

The bittern, like the godwit, has come back to its fens. A hundred years ago it was not quite extinct, like the godwit; but was making a last stand in Norfolk, having previously bred in quite a wide area as far north as the Lowlands, wherever there were suitable large marshes. After 1868 it only bred once, during the nineteenth century. It was given up as lost. Then, in 1911, Miss E. L. Turner discovered a pair in the Broads once more. Since then the bittern has gradually increased; to-day it breeds in Suffolk and Cambridgeshire, as well as in Norfolk.

The bearded tit formerly bred in six East Anglian counties, as well as in Kent and Sussex, and Devon. Now it is restricted to Norfolk and Suffolk. Just lately it may have returned, as a breeding bird, to another county. Never present in large numbers in any one place, the bearded tit has had considerable fluctuations in numbers; the cold winters of 1940-42 did not help its status

27

very much. It seems, however, pretty certain that the species will now survive in Britain, in spite of the effect of sudden cold winters, and the restriction of its habitat.

The disappearance of the big fens, and of some of their birds, is a change rather different—as far as the birds are concerned—from the other changes we have described. The birds of the woodland-agricultural land successions in many cases adapted themselves to the change, by settling in the new habitat that succeeded the old. But marshland birds do not appear to be able to adapt themselves to woodland, or open tillage. They are too specialised. Hence they have either gone; or have hung on to, or have returned to what little was left. They have never struck out in other directions.

LATE CHANGES

IT is not easy to invent a heading to attach to some of the further changes that have taken place in British bird life. *Late changes* will do perhaps, because it is only in the last two hundred years or so, that we can trace changes due to man's sport and man's habit of making collections; and it is only in such a period that natural history records have been complete, or accurate enough, to enable us to trace other changes in the status of certain birds, which cannot be directly attributed to alterations in habitat or the activities of man.

William the Conqueror in Britain did not hesitate to depopulate huge areas, in order to improve hunting forests, and the chase; the hunting was to be for him—and it was to be so for King John who, in 1209, forbade, entirely, the taking of birds throughout Britain. In 1389, under Richard II, anybody

Hirundo apus.
The black Martin
or Swift.

Hirundo domestica.
The common house Swallow.

Hirundo agrestis seu rustica.
The Martin or
Martlet.

Hirundo riparia.
The Bank Martin.

Ruticilla.
The Redstart.

Rubecula.
The Robin-red
Breast.

Hirundo domestica

W. Faithorne f.

SWIFT, SWALLOWS, HOUSE MARTIN, SAND MARTIN, REDSTART, ROBIN
Wood engraving by W. Faithorne, 1676

qualified by estate could kill game; the qualifications, naturally, varied, but the principle remained in force until the Game Act of 1831, which permitted anybody to kill game (unless this involved trespass) by obtaining a licence. Nevertheless it is true to say that the pursuit of game and game birds remains to this day an activity of the landowning and farming classes. The game rights of an estate remain an important asset, a commodity to be leased—and taxed on the value of the lease; the preservation of game, and the showing of sport remains an important, rather feudal minor industry.

The pursuit of game in Britain has affected bird life in two very important ways. Man has concerned himself busily with the management of his game birds; and with the control of the birds that prey on them—or those which he believes to prey on them. Discarding, for the moment, the strict notion of what is game within the meaning of the act, we can say that, in Britain, men take an interest in the pursuit of pheasants, partridges, red-legged partridges; grouse, black game, ptarmigan, capercaillie; several species of geese and ducks; three species of pigeons; many species of waders, especially woodcock and snipe. If quail and corncrakes were not now rare, they would no doubt feature on this list; and I believe that the extinct great bustard is still legally game.

Of these birds, the pheasant was probably introduced in Roman times, certainly before the Conquest; the French partridge was brought to Suffolk in about 1770; the caper has been reintroduced. Until the eighteenth century, game, in general, was hunted by individuals, and by stealth. There was no science of game management, or game preservation—no technique of driving, or much practice of beating. The pheasant was a rare, wild bird—not an abundant, and sometimes almost domestic creature. Man shared the pursuit of game with the wolf, the sweetmart, the foumart, the cat, the fox, the large birds of prey. He did not, then, resent their competition very much. Until the end of the seventeenth century he scarcely used firearms at all, in Britain— his game fell to the longbow and the crossbow.

The use of firearms in sport has caused such a series of minor revolutions and upheavals in the British bird fauna that it is necessary to trace its evolution with some care. By the time sporting arms began to be used in Britain the shot gun had passed through several stages of its evolution. Guns had fired at game, on the continent, in the fifteenth century. The wheel lock was invented at the beginning of the sixteenth; and a sort of breech loader as early as 1537. In 1533 wildfowl were killed with guns in Norfolk; though crossbows were mainly used. In 1586 a cartridge had been devised, for the muzzleloaders of those days. Though guns did begin to get made, in Birmingham, in 1603, the main craft centred round Paris. The firelock, or flintlock, was invented in 1635, and by the middle of the century breech-loading flintlocks, turned out with beautiful craftsmanship in France, began to reach Britain. By the end of the century their use had become general in British sport. By the beginning of the next century this was most probably beginning to have its effect on the game population.

30

GOLDEN EAGLE
Drawing by J. Wolf, 1888

There can be little doubt that man has passed through three stages in his attitude to sport. First, armed with his crossbow or wheel-lock, he was the simple hunter, taking his chance, on his estate, with what he could find. His servants, to whom he deputed the lesser hunting, the fishing and snaring, were not keepers in any positive sense.

The second stage lasted for a century and a half; from 1700 until 1861, when the central-fire, percussion cartridge was introduced. The sportsman's servants, in this period, became keepers, and their activities resulted in the decline of the birds of prey; this decline continued into the third period, when the efficiency of firearms and the evolution of driving demanded still further stocks of game; the keepers had to become more skilled, more scientific, better breeders of game. In this period the pheasant rearing-field, the Euston system of partridge raising, the rotation of heather burning (to ensure new shoots for grouse to feed on) developed. The principle in the first period was, in short, simply to hunt; in the second, to reduce the competing predators and thus increase the prey; in the third, to increase the numbers of prey yet further by artificial conservation.

The application of these principles has certainly had the desired effect. Game, in peace-time Britain, is abundant. In the third period the numbers of grouse reached such dimensions that epidemic disease became an important agent in their control. During the last war 2,929 grouse were shot by one party, in one day, on one moor. Pheasants are everywhere common, and in places as abundant as the suppliers of foster-mothers and fodder care to make them. And the game-preservers have developed clever methods of keeping up the stock of partridges. Unless we count the bustard, which was doomed by the eighteen-thirties, the only game which is beyond the control of the preserver is blackcock, corncrake, quail.

If the present abundance of pheasants, grouse and partridges is to be regarded as a credit to our fauna, we must, in fairness, balance this against a considerable debit. Few people realise how radical has been the decline of the birds of prey in the last one hundred and fifty to two hundred years. In the seventeenth and eighteenth centuries kites and buzzards, hen- and marsh harriers, eagles and peregrines, were found over most suitable parts of England, Wales and Scotland. The kite was a common bird at the end of the eighteenth century ; "I only saw . . ." wrote Gilbert White in 1773 of a walk on the Sussex Downs, "several kites and buzzards." A hundred years later the guns and traps had done their work, and the kite was rare. County after county had been cleared altogether ; the birds survived only in remote, wooded foothills. By 1905 the kite population was *five birds*, in Wales. In the later stages there is no doubt that collectors helped the decline. However, the Welsh kite has shown fairly remarkable powers of survival, for a tiny population has held out to the present day. The number of birds is now about 13. Some of these are old and probably past breeding, and in the last few years only one or two broods have safely got off ; I am afraid I am rather pessimistic about the kite's future.

I have already described the present state of the marsh harrier—it seems to be in a worse condition than the kite. Other birds of prey are also making last stands, or what might, if things go badly, be last stands. The hen-harrier has a healthy population now only in Orkney, an outpost in the Outer Hebrides, and a group of apparently roving birds which attempt to nest, from time to time, in the Highlands, Ireland and Wales—sometimes with fair success. But the days when the hen-harrier played an important part in the animal community of most of the upland moors of Britain, are gone. Gone also is the eagle, the golden eagle, from all Britain but the Highlands. Here, even, it has suffered from persecution and collectors, though less now. Luckily a good many deer-forest owners like it—it keeps down the grouse which disturb the deer—which means that the bird protection laws get a chance of being enforced. There are plenty in Sutherland and Ross, and a fair number in Inverness, Argyll and Aberdeenshire. The sea-eagle has gone altogether ; the last pair bred on the Noup of Noss in Shetland until 1908, when the male was shot. The female brooded the empty site every year for ten more years.

Peregrines and buzzards have also suffered—though they have not been driven out of so many areas. They are still safe members of the fauna of these islands, however. Buzzards, in fact, have been increasing of late very rapidly. In the West Country there are now plenty, and they have lately spread to the Outer Hebrides. Buzzards are coming back well.

It is now clear that in the last couple of hundred years there were considerable upheavals in our bird fauna, through the direct interference of man. This inter-

GOLDFINCHES

Illustration by John Gould, 1863, from his *Birds of Great Britain*

PARTRIDGE AND CHICKS

Illustration by Edward Neale, 1877, from Dresser's *Birds of Europe*

ference grew steadily more intense throughout the period—partly (as regards the birds of prey in particular) through the development of the shotgun ; and (in the second hundred years, mainly) through the rise of the collectors. Towards the birds which had already been made rare, by the restriction of their habitat, or by keepering, the collectors, attracted by this very rarity, turned their closest and most earnest attentions.

Taking what I believe to be a moderate view, it is true to say that the collectors cannot always be blamed for the rarity of certain birds, nor for certain extinctions. But they have made some bad gaps in our fauna, especially in the second half of the last century, when they dominated ornithology, and had very little scientific or political opposition.

To-day people have much less patience, than they had, with collectors who say that they *must* have the skins or eggs of rare British birds. No sensible person wants to stop scientific collection, but it is generally felt that it should be aimed, in future, in the most useful directions. A comparative study of wren or rock pipit skins over a large number of islands and mainland areas would, for instance, be a hundred times more use to zoology than the collection of the skin of the last British osprey, or the eggs of a kite or Temminck's stint.

The only books written about birds' eggs, in this country in this century, which are of any importance from the point of view of general zoology and science, all concern the problems of the cuckoo—one of the few zoological matters on which egg-collecting has thrown any *direct* light. On the other hand, by the very fact of being egg-collectors, some ornithologists have become first-rate field bird-watchers. Though they may not have got started, unless by collecting eggs, there is no evidence that they would be any worse ornithologists if they now gave up the collecting of great rarities—as some, in fact, have done.

Let me give a little example of the wanton destruction of rare birds and their eggs, that went on in the last century. Let us consider Charles St. John's adventures in Sutherlandshire, in the summer of 1848. He was after ospreys. Near Scourie he shot the hen of a breeding pair, and took two eggs. At Rhiconich he took, from a nest, one young bird and an addled egg ; he could not shoot the old birds, though he tried hard enough. At another nest near Rhiconich he shot the male, missed the female, and took three young birds. He afterwards found that the male at Scourie had mated again ; its female had laid an egg which he took. And to top it all he ended his account, of the destruction of what was possibly the entire osprey population (save a few survivors) of north-west Sutherland, by saying "There are but very few in Britain at any time, their principal head quarters seeming to be in America ; and though living in tolerable peace in the Highlands, they do not appear to increase nor to breed in any localities excepting where they find a situation for their nest similar to what I have already described [an islet in a lonely loch]. As they in no way interfere with the sportsman or others, it is a great pity that they should ever be destroyed."

The ospreys got destroyed, all right, by the likes of Mr. St. John. It did not take very long. Let us balance our quotation from St. John by another, from Witherby's new *Handbook of British Birds*; which gives the osprey's obituary.

"Formerly summer-resident in a good many places in Scotland, but now extinct as breeding species. Last bred at Loch Arkaig in 1902 and single bird there until 1910; last bred at Loch an Eilein in 1899 and in 1901 and 1902 only a single bird, after these dates both these localities forsaken. There is evidence of breeding at Loch Luichart and elsewhere on occasions since, but we have not definite proof of this."

In the very latest years of the nineteenth century groups of the more enlightened ornithologists began to realise that positive measures would have to be taken, to stop the disappearance of rare birds. They knew that some fast-disappearing habitats would have to be saved, or at least a part of them; and they knew that the more intransigeant collectors would have to be fought. In Norfolk the battle started in 1888, and went well. The Wild Birds' Protection Committee of the Norfolk Naturalists' Trust now manages some fine tracts of marsh and saltings, which have become famous as a safe resort of rare migrants, waders and wildfowl. The Royal Society for the Protection of Birds, formed in 1889, now has watchers and sanctuaries and interests in many parts of the country Quite a number of birds have been saved from extinction, or near-extinction, by the preservation and watching of their haunts—or even, in some special cases, the policing of individual nests. To the tireless work of watchers and wardens we must attribute the present good numbers of the great skua in Shetland, the hen-harrier in Orkney, the bittern in the Broads, the terns at Scolt Head and Blakeney. Each kite's nest in central Wales has been guarded by a special watcher, in recent years—at considerable expense.

After fifty years of bird protection, some of the birds are coming back, that we thought were lost.

It would not be proper to conclude a summary of this sort without pointing out the fact that some of the recent changes in the status of British birds cannot be proved to have much to do with the direct or indirect interference of man. For instance, it has been suggested that the disappearance of the wryneck from southern England (it is now a *very* rare bird) may be due to the lack of pollard apple trees, in which it used to nest; but this suggestion cannot bear very close examination. All efforts at correlating the remarkable decrease of the corn-crake in recent years with changes in the technique of mowing and the use of basic slag as fertiliser seem to have been rather fruitless, so far. In the last hundred years the gannets of Britain reached their lowest number; by 1889 they were down to just over seventy thousand birds. They have been gradually increasing since then, and had reached in 1939 a total just under one hundred and ten thousand. This increase can be fairly attributed to the long-term effect of leaving the birds in peace. They have only been seriously persecuted in the twentieth century in two places in Britain, and are now taken only at

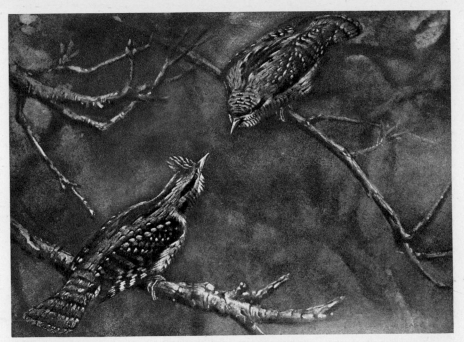

WRYNECKS, POSTURING
Water colour drawing by A. W. Seaby, c. 1909

one colony. On the other hand, the increase of the fulmar, which has been far more spectacular, is due to a biological change, perhaps in the bird's habits, which is not properly understood. One thing we do know, about the fulmar's spread, is that it has had little to do with the habits of man on St. Kilda, where it was a staple article of diet well into the present century. It was previously suggested that, at the time when the great spread started, the St. Kildans began to eat imported foods instead of fulmars, so that the birds increased. This has now been proved, pretty conclusively, to have not been so.

Birds do undoubtedly change their habits. It is not easy always to tell why, or how, they do this. We do not know why the fulmar has spread, and started to nest in what were once abnormal nesting places. We do not know why the curlew or the redshank have spread, or why the black redstart never bred in England before 1923. As I write, in midsummer 1942, intelligence comes of black redstarts in several English towns; of about twelve singing males in central London, releasing their reeling song, with its sneeze-like note in the middle, from roofs overlooking bombed-out sites; at this moment London's ornithologists are seeking nests in the blitzed City, and among the ruins of the burnt-out Guildhall. The British would welcome more such invasions.

UNTIL some time after the middle ages, the only people capable of making records of bird life, and giving us any sort of picture of it, were the monks and lords, and their educated servants. To them, fairly naturally, birds were economic creatures ; those of which they spoke were large and edible, or birds of prey. Practically all the literature, in fact, was about hawking. Such generalised observations as were made, about the habits of birds, were copied by monks from Pliny and Aristotle. England did not appear, in the middle ages, to be interested enough to breed original observers. Small birds were of no note, unless they robbed orchards ; for this economic reason, alone, Matthew Paris gives us an account of a crossbill invasion in 1251. Until 1544, when Turner wrote, there was no book, or treatise, on the birds of Britain, that was original or scientific.

It is an interesting coincidence that two of the naturalists who did as much as anybody, and more than most, to establish the study of wild creatures in Britain, applied unsuccessfully for election to the Provostship of Oriel College, Oxford, and were members of the Anglican clergy. It is perhaps just as well that William Turner and, exactly two hundred years later, Gilbert White, failed to achieve this academic honour, for it is clear that their lives were best devoted to the pursuit of birds, and the description of their distribution and habits.

Turner was the first critical naturalist. Not content, as were his predecessors and many of his successors, to copy, simply, from Aristotle and Pliny, he set himself the task of determining exactly what the birds named by these men were, and of adding notes on such of them as had come under his own, *personal*, observation. We owe a lot to Turner and, incidentally to A. H. Evans, whose translation, in 1903, rescued the *Avium Precipuarum* from rarity and comparative obscurity.

Turner was thought highly of in his own time. Gesner, whose *Historia Animalium* was published in 1555, was a friend of his, and quoted a good deal from him in his book. This book had many woodcuts, some excellent, others perfectly frightful. Dr. John Kay, who kept a puffin in his house for eight months (which is longer than most aviculturists can manage) published notes of some originality in 1570. In 1577 a canon of Windsor, William Harrison, published what is, to all intents and purposes, the first List of British Birds— as a prefix to Holinshed's Chronicle. Parts of it were good and full of original information, about the status of birds—good enough for comparison with later status.

The sixteenth century then, brought us the first accounts of the birds of Britain that were truly accurate or objective. The clerics, Turner and Harrison, set down what they knew about birds, for its own sake, and for no other motive, as far as anybody can discover. Incidentally, they started the clerical

EIDERS COURTING
Drawing by J. G. Millais, 1913

tradition ; for three hundred years after Turner published, the clergy and certain lay dons more or less took over the observing and recording of nature— only in the last hundred years, since Darwin, has the laity played any great part.

Of the seventeenth century naturalists, Sir Thomas Browne is important, if not for his accounts of game, wildfowl and birds of prey, then for his sensible and balanced views on migration. He wrote in 1662, and his views in this respect were more correct, less puzzled, perhaps, than Gilbert White's, a century later. Some of his contemporaries, with whom he corresponded, like Merrett and John Evelyn were, as regards natural history, minor figures. Not so, however, was John Ray. Between 1658 and 1662, Ray, and his eminent friend Francis Willughby, journeyed through much of England, Wales and Scotland, purely in search of living things. From 1663 to 1666 they were on the continent. In 1667 they were in Cornwall. In 1672 Willughby died—he was only thirty-seven ; and in 1676 Ray brought out the *Ornithologia* of Willughby, which, though published under Willughby's name and, on paper, only edited by Ray, was in fact a work of partnership, a partnership in which Ray was the senior member. It was the first standard, illustrated, textbook of the birds of the British Isles.

The eighteenth century was notable in that the naturalists became concerned with a new question. Though Ray and Willughby followed rather a careful order in their setting out of the various species of birds that were known to them, they cannot be said to have treated classification as a science, or troubled much about it as an end in itself. In the eighteenth century, however, the special study of classification began. In a sense, this study was a product of the early empires and exploitations of the new countries ; the specimens that the explorers brought home, and the improvements in the technique of preservation, made it very necessary to invent a science of natural arrangement. Linnaeus of Sweden invented the binomial system of naming animals and plants that has been in use ever since he published the first list of names in 1758. It is fair to say that all the eighteenth century naturalists, with the exception of Gilbert White, concentrated on descriptions and names. They were so keen to get the recognition of animals cut and dried that they nearly all put studies and accounts of the creatures in the field, into second place. None of them, with the possible exception of Bishop Pontoppidan, were such observant field-naturalists as their predecessors Turner or Ray, or their contemporary Gilbert White.

In the eighteenth century, Gilbert White is the dominant figure. He over-shadows the lesser British faunists of his time, like Berkenhout, Tunstall, Walcott, Donovan—though these produced some useful picture-books. The more important contemporary faunist, Thomas Pennant, began to bring out his *British Zoology* in 1766. In the following year White began his famous correspondence with Pennant, who was quick to use the information and observations in new parts of his work. Pennant, to give him his due, was an indefatigable worker, com-

SAND MARTINS GATHERING
Drawing by John Gould, engraved by W. Hart, 1863

piler and traveller. He knew his geography, and his libraries, well. He was more learned, in the strict sense, than White. And he was a fine naturalist. But somehow he is always remembered as the man White wrote letters to. As for White, his *Natural History of Selborne*, first published in December 1788, has had so many editions that they are rather difficult to count. There are probably 145 (up to March, 1941). It is the classic British nature book. It is full of new discoveries, recounted without any obvious pride or emotion. Perhaps unconsciously, White used the perfect scientific method ; in his accounts and arguments there is nothing preconceived.

For Gilbert White, for the natural history knowledge that he unlocked, and for the existence and work of a regular school of his successors, we have to thank the system of bestowment of Church livings. No other, better system could have been devised for placing educated, simple, honourable, truthful and contemplative men in the places where they were needed most—dotted evenly all over the countryside, where they could record nature. Without the clergy our knowledge of nature in Britain at all ages, but most particularly up to the end of the nineteenth century would, quite simply, have been poor instead of rich. To give an example, the clergy of nearly a thousand Scottish parishes were invited to give accounts of their areas in the *Statistical Account of Scotland* (published between 1791 and 1797), and again in the *New Statistical Account* (published in 1845, but mainly written in the eighteen-thirties). Nearly a hundred of them, on each occasion, make quite a bit of the heading 'natural history' provided for them; some of their accounts form the basis of our present knowledge of changes in the Scottish bird fauna; many of their writings are full of enthusiasm, and a real feeling for nature.

A further pointer to the importance of the Anglican and Scottish clergy, as recorders of nature, is the fact that there was no parallel movement in Ireland. It is fair to say that we know extraordinarily little about Irish natural history of a hundred and more years ago; and it is fair to suggest that this was because there was nobody to take any interest, or write anything down. The parish priests were not interested in animals, and took no notice of birds. They differed (and still differ) in many ways from the British clergy; in their outlook, in their education, in their social antecedents, in the type of work they were expected to do and the type of things they were expected to be interested in. It is safe to say that only lately has this generalisation—about the natural history knowledge of the Catholic priests—begun to be untrue.

We cannot properly leave the eighteenth century without some mention of two other contemporaries of White's. Latham, a great classifier, began to publish in 1781; his influence is mainly academic, but quite important. Bewick of Newcastle, who first published in 1797, is famous and popular for being the first great illustrator of birds. He was a real naturalist, and a real artist. In his woodcuts he brought birds to life. His works were, and still are, in huge demand; with White he gave an enormous impetus to the popular study of birds.

It is not surprising, then, that in the nineteenth century the most successful works should have had, as their object, the cataloguing of what was known about British birds, their accurate depiction in plates, often coloured, and their accurate description in text. For the amateur ornithologist was beginning to become an important consumer of bird books, and a contributor of much minor information. And the amateur collections of eggs, and sometimes of skins, began to accumulate. Hence the appearance of that excellent and original work, Montagu's *Ornithological Dictionary* in 1802; of McGillivray's fine textbook in 1837; of Yarrell's illustrated textbook (which became the standard one) in 1843; of Hancock's edition of Bewick in 1847; finally, of John Gould's superb plates from 1862 to 1873 (some of these were by the great animal painter, Joseph Wolf). In this period descriptive ornithology reached its height; since then, in British ornithology, there has been very little improvement in methods of description (except in the description of characters of birds *in the field*) and practically no improvement in plates (though there have been recent attempts to illustrate *habits*, e.g. courtship, combat). Since the days of Gould and Wolf there has been only one really important bird artist in Britain, Archibald Thorburn; Thorburn was just about as good as Gould, and held his position as the leading (sometimes the only) British bird artist from about 1885, until his death in 1935. There have been few others, during or since the period when Thorburn flourished—unless we except the rather academic workers,

DARTFORD WARBLERS
Illustration by J. G. Keulemans
From Lilford's *Coloured Figures of the Birds of the British Islands,* 1887

RED GROUSE

Illustration by Archibald Thorburn, 1908, from Millais' *Natural History of British Game Birds*

Neale, Keulemans, Grönvold, the modern illustrators, Lodge, Seaby, Harrison, Talbot Kelly, and the wildfowl specialist Peter Scott—who could draw or paint birds in a worthy manner.

By the end of the nineteenth century the zoologists had completely taken over scientific ornithology. An ornithologist, Alfred Newton, was in the Professorial Chair at Cambridge. The British Ornithologists' Union was a strong, progressive, learned body. The great collections were accumulating, still partly in private hands, but mainly in the Bird Room of the British Museum, and in the Rothschild Museum at Tring. The text books were kept carefully up-to-date. The management of ornithological affairs was, generally speaking, in the hands of a body of University-trained, academic men, to whom was attached a large group of highly-educated, often wealthy, lay enthusiasts. The general trend of bird science was still in the directions of classification and geographical distribution.

To-day, in the twentieth century, there is still plenty of the academic tradition in ornithology. Few people could object to this. But many new things have happened. For instance, the classification, and enumeration of the British species is now so cut and dried, that the attention of the classifiers is now devoted entirely to subspecies, rather than species, or even to small populations of birds in restricted areas. Now that the spadework of classification has been done, and now that geographical distributions have been very adequately worked out (the modern *Handbook*, the last volume of which came out in 1941, shows the state to which these matters have got) bird watchers have been more and more turning their attention to the habits of birds, to their numbers, and to their relations with their environment and the other living things around them. Under the name of ecology, studies of field natural history are being made once again. Animal psychologists are devoting their attention to the territorial and breeding habits of birds, and to their selection of habitats. Statisticians are estimating the populations of woodland, moorland, agricultural birds, and the numbers of grebes, herons, gannets, fulmars. Writers on nature now set out their accounts and descriptions with unsentimental accuracy, but with hints of a new, budding romanticism. Indeed the study of living things is being pursued by more people, with more vigour and imagination than ever before.

The growth of a public interest in natural history has been obvious since the first world war. During the second struggle it increased, rather than slackened. The scientists, busy collecting facts about birds in the field, have welcomed this. For instance one national organisation, the British Trust for Ornithology, was started in 1933 with the object of putting this great public interest to use, by conducting co-operative field observations. To-day it sends out questionnaires to over a thousand members, belonging to all classes and living in all parts of Britain, who pay their annual subscriptions for the privilege of filling in the forms with what information they have to give. Without the work of Trust members, and the co-operation of all sorts of people from lighthouse-keepers to landowners, we would not know half the amount we do about the present distribution of the fulmar. Over two thousand people give the Trust information about the decrease of the corncrake. Perhaps a hundred make routine visits, every year, to the majority of the English and Welsh breeding sites of the heron, and count the nests. Officers and men in His Majesty's Ships send in their notes of birds seen at sea ; aircraft of the Coastal Command fly over remote rocks and islands and take photographs of the breeding birds, for analysis by ornithologists ; men in the army, stationed all over the world, keep touch with their organisations in Britain and keep them supplied with new information about birds.

There can be no possible doubt that the section of the British public which is interested in birds is *really* large. In cold numbers it certainly amounts to over a hundred thousand ; possibly over a million. Such people know most of the fifty or so commonest birds apart ; often take the trouble to look up, in some textbook, a bird strange to them ; know the songs of a dozen species ; read popular works on birds ; buy a bird picture or two. Many of these people are quite prepared to take political action, if they think that interesting species of birds are in danger, or if they think that there are unnecessary obstructions to the pursuit of their hobby. Hence it is of importance to record that the subject of nature preservation in post-war reconstruction is receiving some attention from the Government at the moment. If, very soon, areas are set apart as National parks ; and, within these areas and elsewhere, sanctuaries for birds, for all time, are established (beyond those which exist already) it is more than likely that we will save some of the species that are fading away ; attract back to us some that have already gone ; and, who knows, perhaps attract some that have never belonged to the British fauna before.

PIED WAGTAILS' DISPLAY
Drawing by G. E. Lodge, 1929

RED-BREASTED MERGANSERS
Water colour drawing by A. Thorburn, 1912

HOODED CROW
Wood engraving by A. Fussell and J. Thompson, 1839

THE FUTURE

WHAT will happen to British birds, and British bird-watchers, during the rest of this century?

I think it is possible to be optimistic about the birds. They will come to less harm than before. Changes in their status will be noted with more care, and predicted with more accuracy. Man will have more power to stop, or encourage, these changes ; more power to conserve them for his own study and edification.

As for man's attitude to birds, I suggest that it will become more romantic, more familiar, less sentimental, less ignorant. Bird scientists will be able, with their armies of lay helpers, to conduct a great Mass Observation of birds ; perhaps even a school of bird painters may rise again, to do justice to British wild life once more. Birds will never become more important, economically. Thus in all probability the artificial balance caused by the preservation of game will alter, and the birds of prey will (though slowly) rise again. Many would like to see them back. The little birds of the fields and hedges, nearly all friends of the farmer and enemies of insects, will suffer less from human ignorance. The few bird enemies of man, like the woodpigeon, will be gradually conquered and reduced to the status of interestingly rare, rather than injurious species.

Children of all ages will learn, in school, the art and science of bird study and conservation.

The new natural history will have much organisation, much propaganda. The county natural history societies will revive ; their records will become more regular and accurate, their recorders more conscientious. School-children will be given responsible work to do ; will be trained in observation and note-taking. In the field, birds will be watched from on foot, from cars, from boats and ships, from aircraft. The records will pour in to the national centres, where they will be collated, sifted, criticised, sorted, embodied in textbooks. Some mechanical method of collecting, sorting and presenting knowledge may be necessary ; perhaps one day, not very far ahead, some zoologist may press a button in London or Oxford or Cambridge or Aberystwyth or Edinburgh, a machine will hum, and a stack of cards giving all the records of crossbill irruptions in East Anglia, or the history of the pied flycatcher in Wales, or the migrations of the woodpigeon in Scotland, will fall into a tray. At the rate records are coming in, even now, such machines appear to be necessary. They are quite a practical proposition.

To sum up : for the rest of this century the British naturalists are going to be increasingly out of doors, enjoying and assessing the wealth of British birds, and other living things. The British countryside, less exploited, more loved and cared for, will be their playground. For the study of birds is play ; a science often, an art sometimes, but still play. And who shall stop the British at their honest play ?

GREAT NORTHERN DIVERS
Wood engraving by A. Fussell and J. Thompson, 1842

A LIST OF BRITISH BIRDS

(Complete to 1941)

1. *Residents* : birds which breed, and also winter in Britain (135).

RAVEN
HOODED CROW
CARRION CROW
ROOK
JACKDAW
MAGPIE
JAY
CHOUGH
STARLING
HAWFINCH
GREENFINCH
GOLDFINCH
SISKIN
LESSER REDPOLL
TWITE
LINNET
BULLFINCH
CROSSBILL
CHAFFINCH
CORN BUNTING
YELLOW BUNTING
CIRL BUNTING
REED BUNTING
SNOW BUNTING
HOUSE SPARROW
TREE SPARROW
WOODLARK
SKYLARK
MEADOW PIPIT
ROCK PIPIT
GREY WAGTAIL
PIED WAGTAIL
TREE-CREEPER
NUTHATCH
GREAT TIT
BLUE TIT

COAL TIT
CRESTED TIT
MARSH TIT
WILLOW TIT
LONG-TAILED TIT
BEARDED TIT
GOLDCREST
DARTFORD WARBLER
MISTLE THRUSH
SONG THRUSH
BLACKBIRD
STONECHAT
BLACK REDSTART
ROBIN
HEDGE SPARROW
WREN
DIPPER
KINGFISHER
GREEN WOODPECKER
GREAT SPOTTED
  WOODPECKER
LESSER SPOTTED
  WOODPECKER
LITTLE OWL
LONG-EARED OWL
SHORT-EARED OWL
TAWNY OWL
BARN OWL
PEREGRINE FALCON
MERLIN
KESTREL
GOLDEN EAGLE
COMMON BUZZARD
MARSH HARRIER
HEN HARRIER
SPARROW HAWK

KITE
COMMON HERON
BITTERN
WHOOPER SWAN
MUTE SWAN
GREY LAG GOOSE
CANADA GOOSE
SHELD DUCK
MALLARD
GADWALL
TEAL
WIGEON
PINTAIL
SHOVELER
COMMON POCHARD
TUFTED DUCK
SCAUP
COMMON EIDER
COMMON SCOTER
GOOSANDER
RED-BREASTED
  MERGANSER
CORMORANT
SHAG
GANNET
STORM PETREL
LEACH'S FORK-TAILED
  PETREL
MANX SHEARWATER
FULMAR
GREAT CRESTED GREBE
SLAVONIAN GREBE
BLACK-NECKED GREBE
LITTLE GREBE
BLACK-THROATED DIVER

RED-THROATED DIVER
WOODPIGEON
STOCKDOVE
ROCKDOVE
BLACK-TAILED
  GODWIT
CURLEW
WOODCOCK
SNIPE
REDSHANK
RINGED PLOVER
GOLDEN PLOVER
LAPWING
OYSTERCATCHER
BLACK-HEADED GULL
COMMON GULL
HERRING GULL
GREAT BLACK-BACKED
  GULL
KITTIWAKE
RAZORBILL
GUILLEMOT
BLACK GUILLEMOT
PUFFIN
WATER RAIL
MOORHEN
COOT
CAPERCAILLIE
BLACK GROUSE
RED GROUSE
PTARMIGAN
PHEASANT
PARTRIDGE
RED-LEGGED
  PARTRIDGE

2. *Residents* now extinct (1).

GREAT AUK

3. *Summer visitors* which come to Britain to breed (51).

TREE PIPIT
YELLOW WAGTAIL
RED-BACKED SHRIKE
SPOTTED
  FLYCATCHER
PIED FLYCATCHER
CHIFFCHAFF
WILLOW WARBLER
WOOD WARBLER
GRASSHOPPER
  WARBLER

REED WARBLER
MARSH WARBLER
SEDGE WARBLER
GARDEN WARBLER
BLACKCAP
WHITETHROAT
LESSER WHITETHROAT
RING OUZEL
WHEATEAR
WHINCHAT
REDSTART

NIGHTINGALE
SWALLOW
HOUSE MARTIN
SAND MARTIN
SWIFT
NIGHTJAR
WRYNECK
CUCKOO
HOBBY
MONTAGU'S HARRIER
GARGANEY

TURTLEDOVE
WHIMBREL
RED-NECKED
  PHALAROPE
DUNLIN
COMMON SANDPIPER
GREENSHANK
KENTISH PLOVER
DOTTEREL
STONE CURLEW
SANDWICH TERN

ROSEATE TERN	LITTLE TERN	GREAT SKUA	SPOTTED CRAKE
COMMON TERN	LESSER BLACK-BACKED	ARCTIC SKUA	QUAIL
ARCTIC TERN	GULL	CORNCRAKE	

4. *Summer visitors* which come to Britain, having bred in the south (2).

GREAT SHEARWATER
SOOTY SHEARWATER

5. *Winter visitors* (26).

BRAMBLING	BEWICK'S SWAN	VELVET SCOTER	PURPLE SANDPIPER
SHORELARK	WHITE-FRONTED	SMEW	GREY PLOVER
WAXWING	GOOSE	RED-NECKED GREBE	LITTLE GULL
FIRECREST	BEAN GOOSE*	GREAT NORTHERN	GLAUCOUS GULL
FIELDFARE	BARNACLE GOOSE	DIVER	ICELAND GULL
REDWING	BRENT GOOSE	JACK SNIPE	(*with which is included
ROUGH-LEGGED	GOLDENEYE	TURNSTONE	PINK-FOOTED GOOSE)
BUZZARD	LONG-TAILED DUCK	KNOT	

6. *Passage migrants* (22).

GOLDEN ORIOLE	BLUETHROAT	GREY PHALAROPE	GREEN SANDPIPER
ORTOLAN BUNTING	HOOPOE	CURLEW SANDPIPER	SPOTTED REDSHANK
LITTLE BUNTING	HONEY BUZZARD	LITTLE STINT	AVOCET
LAPLAND BUNTING	OSPREY	SANDERLING	BLACK TERN
BARRED WARBLER	SPOONBILL	RUFF	POMATORHINE SKUA
	BAR-TAILED GODWIT	WOOD SANDPIPER	

7. *Scarce or irregular visitors, and vagrants* (100).

NUTCRACKER	GREAT REED	GREAT WHITE HERON	LITTLE RINGED
ROSE-COLOURED	WARBLER	LITTLE EGRET	PLOVER
STARLING	BLYTH'S REED	SQUACCO HERON	AMERICAN GOLDEN
HORNEMAN'S	WARBLER	NIGHT HERON	PLOVER
REDPOLL	AQUATIC WARBLER	LITTLE BITTERN	SOCIABLE PLOVER
SERIN	ICTERINE WARBLER	AMERICAN BITTERN	BLACK-WINGED STILT
SCARLET GROSBEAK	MELODIOUS WARBLER	FLAMINGO	CREAM-COLOURED
PINE GROSBEAK	WHITE'S THRUSH	SNOW GOOSE	COURSER
PARROT CROSSBILL	DUSKY THRUSH	RED-BREASTED GOOSE	PRATINCOLE
TWO-BARRED	BLACK-EARED	RUDDY SHELD DUCK	BLACK-WINGED
CROSSBILL	WHEATEAR	AMERICAN WIGEON	PRATINCOLE
BLACK-HEADED	ALPINE ACCENTOR	RED-CRESTED	GREAT BUSTARD
BUNTING	ALPINE SWIFT	POCHARD	LITTLE BUSTARD
RUSTIC BUNTING	BEE-EATER	FERRUGINOUS DUCK	CRANE
WHITE-WINGED LARK	ROLLER	KING EIDER	WHISKERED TERN
BLACK LARK	YELLOW-BILLED	SURF SCOTER	WHITE-WINGED
SHORT-TOED LARK	CUCKOO	WILSON'S PETREL	BLACK TERN
CRESTED LARK	SNOWY OWL	PALLAS' SAND GROUSE	GULL-BILLED TERN
RICHARD'S PIPIT	EAGLE OWL	BARTRAM'S SANDPIPER	CASPIAN TERN
TAWNY PIPIT	TENGMALM'S OWL	GREAT SNIPE	SABINE'S GULL
RED-THROATED PIPIT	SCOPS OWL	RED-BREASTED SNIPE	MEDITERRANEAN
PETCHORA PIPIT	GYR FALCON	TEMMINCK'S STINT	BLACK-HEADED GULL
WALL-CREEPER	LESSER KESTREL	AMERICAN PECTORAL	IVORY GULL
LESSER GREY SHRIKE	RED-FOOTED FALCON	SANDPIPER	LONG-TAILED SKUA
GREAT GREY SHRIKE	SPOTTED EAGLE	BONAPARTE'S	BRÜNNICH'S
WOODCHAT SHRIKE	GOSHAWK	SANDPIPER	GUILLEMOT
RED-BREASTED	WHITE-TAILED EAGLE	BUFF-BREASTED	LITTLE AUK
FLYCATCHER	WHITE STORK	SANDPIPER	LITTLE CRAKE
YELLOW-BROWED	BLACK STORK	BROAD-BILLED	BAILLON'S CRAKE
WARBLER	GLOSSY IBIS	SANDPIPER	
SAVI'S WARBLER	PURPLE HERON	SPOTTED SANDPIPER	

8. Birds which have been reliably recorded in Britain a dozen times or less but more than once (61).

YELLOW-BREASTED BUNTING
ROCK BUNTING
SNOW FINCH
CALANDRA LARK
COLLARED FLYCATCHER
EVERSMANN'S WARBLER
DUSKY WARBLER
CETTI'S WARBLER
LANCEOLATED WARBLER
OLIVACEOUS WARBLER
ORPHEAN WARBLER
RÜPPELL'S WARBLER
SARDINIAN WARBLER
SUBALPINE WARBLER
RUFOUS WARBLER
ROCK THRUSH

BLACK-THROATED THRUSH
DESERT WHEATEAR
PIED WHEATEAR
ISABELLINE WHEATEAR
BLACK WHEATEAR
THRUSH NIGHTINGALE
RED-RUMPED SWALLOW
NEEDLE-TAILED SWIFT
GREAT SPOTTED CUCKOO
BLACK-BILLED CUCKOO
HAWK OWL
PALLID HARRIER
BLACK KITE
GRIFFON VULTURE

EGYPTIAN VULTURE
BUFF-BACKED HERON
BLUE-WINGED TEAL
BUFFEL-HEADED DUCK
HARLEQUIN DUCK
STELLER'S EIDER
HOODED MERGANSER
MADEIRAN FORK-TAILED PETREL
FRIGATE PETREL
LITTLE SHEARWATER
NORTH ATLANTIC SHEARWATER
BULWER'S PETREL
WHITE-BILLED NORTHERN DIVER
ESKIMO CURLEW
SLENDER-BILLED CURLEW
AMERICAN STINT

SIBERIAN PECTORAL SANDPIPER
BAIRD'S SANDPIPER
TEREK SANDPIPER
SOLITARY SANDPIPER
YELLOWSHANK
GREATER YELLOWSHANK
MARSH SANDPIPER
GREY-RUMPED SANDPIPER
CASPIAN PLOVER
KILDEER PLOVER
MACQUEEN'S BUSTARD
SOOTY TERN
BONAPARTE'S GULL
GREAT BLACK-HEADED GULL
CAROLINA CRAKE

9. Birds which have been reliably recorded only on one single occasion in the British Isles (26).

CITRIL FINCH
PINE BUNTING
RED-HEADED BUNTING
EAST SIBERIAN MEADOW BUNTING
MASKED SHRIKE
BROWN FLYCATCHER
GREENISH WARBLER
PALLAS'S WARBLER

RADDE'S BUSH WARBLER
MOUSTACHED WARBLER
PALLAS'S GRASS-HOPPER WARBLER
PADDY-FIELD WARBLER
BOOTED WARBLER
EGYPTIAN NIGHTJAR

ALGERIAN RED-NECKED NIGHTJAR
AMERICAN NIGHTJAR
LESSER WHITE-FRONTED GOOSE
AUDUBON'S SHEARWATER
KERMADEC PETREL
CAPPED PETREL
COLLARED PETREL

BLACK-BROWED ALBATROSS
EASTERN RUFOUS TURTLEDOVE
SEMIPALMATED SANDPIPER
BRIDLED TERN
ROSS'S GULL

In the compilation of the above list free use has been made of H. F. Witherby's revised *Check-list of British Birds,* which has a short account of the status of each. It was published in 1941 and is right up-to-date.

5958